THE ULTIMATE MINECRAFT COMIC BOOK

VOLUME 2

STEVE AND THE SWAMP WITCH OF ENDOR

BY
HEROBRINE COMICS

RUN EVERYONE! RUN!

AAAAAAHHHHH!

URRRRRRRGGGHHHHH!

BLAG
BLAG

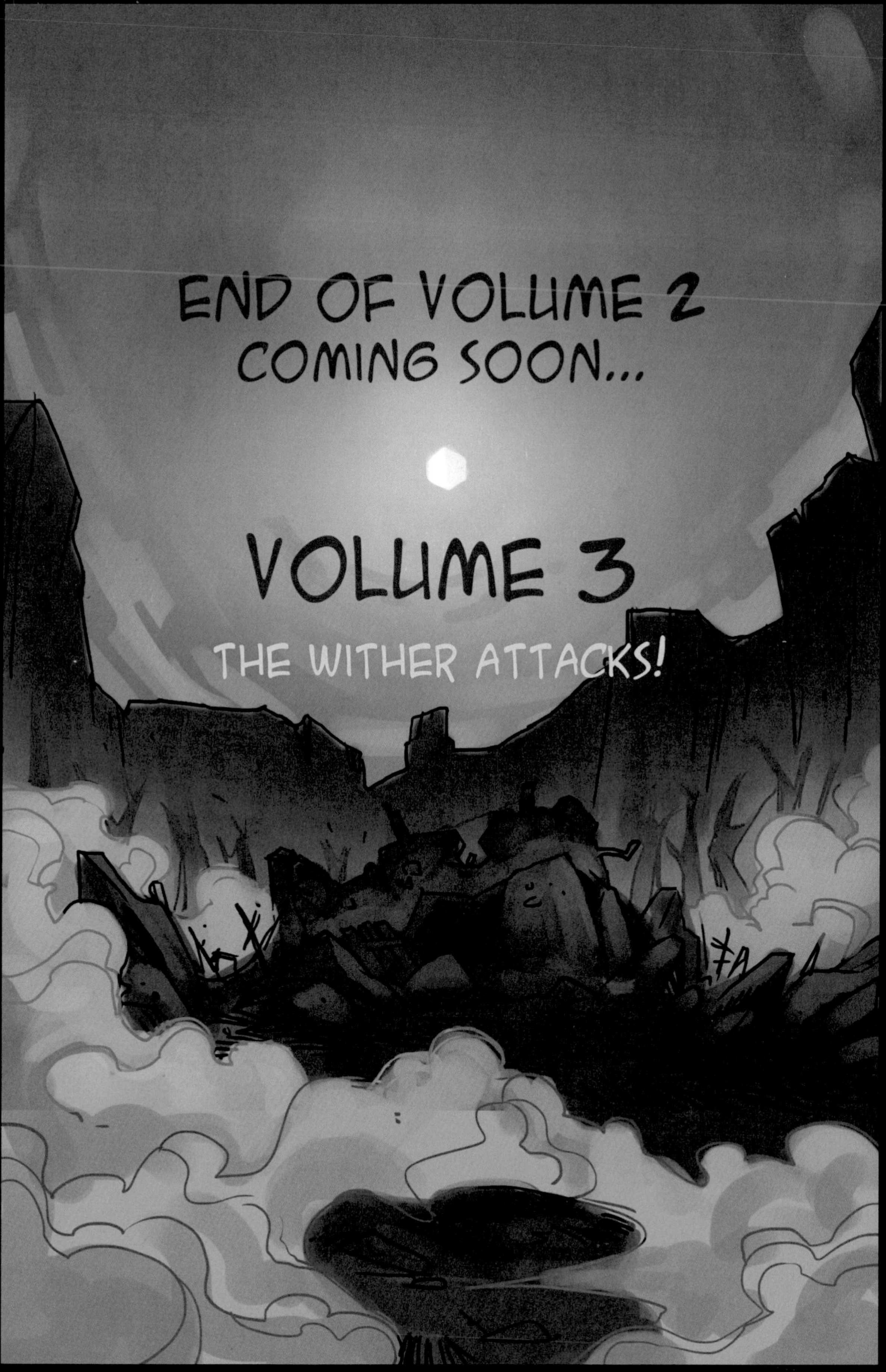
END OF VOLUME 2
COMING SOON...
VOLUME 3
THE WITHER ATTACKS!

Made in the USA
San Bernardino, CA
01 December 2015